St

can read the Speed sounds.

can read the Green words.

can read the Red words.

can read the story.

can answer the questions
bout the story.

. can read the Speed words.

Story 1 My dog Ned

Say the Speed sounds

Consonants

Ask your child to say the sounds (not the letter names) clearly and quickly, in and out of order. Make sure he or she does not add 'uh' to the end of the sounds, e.g. 'f' not 'fuh'.

f	l ll	m	n	r	s	v	z	sh	th	ng nk

b	c k ck	d	g	h	j	p	qu	t	w	x	y	ch

Each box contains one sound.

Vowels

Ask your child to say each vowel sound and then the word, e.g. 'a', 'at'.

at	hen	in	on	up	day	see	high	blow	zoo

4

Read the Green words

*For each word ask your child to read the separate sounds, e.g. 'v-e-t',
'th-i-s' and then blend the sounds together to make the word, e.g. 'vet',
'this'. Sometimes one sound is represented by more than one letter, e.g. 'th',
'sh', 'ck'. These are underlined.*

vet   leg   bad   rub   bit   sit

<u>th</u>is   cra<u>sh</u>   wi<u>ll</u>   his   is   li<u>ck</u>

wag

Read the Red words

*Red words don't sound like they look. Read the words out to your child.
Explain that he or she will have to stop and think about how to say the
red words in the story.*

<u>the</u>   s<u>ai</u>d   I   of   my

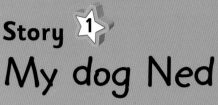

Story 1
My dog Ned

Introduction

Ben has a dog called Ned. One day, Ned starts to limp and feel very sorry for himself so Ben takes him to the vet.

This is Ben. This is Ned.

Ned is Ben's dog.

Ned has a bad leg.

This is the vet.

"My dog has got a bad leg," said Ben.

Ask your child:
⭐ *Why did Ben take Ned to the vet?*

"Sit, Ned," said the vet.

Ned sat.

"I will rub a bit of this on his leg," said the vet.

Rub rub

Sniff sniff

"Get up, Ned,"
said the vet.

Ned got up.

Crash!

"Sit, Ned," said the vet.

Wag wag

Lick lick

Ask your child:
How does Ned feel now?

Speed words for Story ①

Ask your child to read the words across the rows, down the columns and in and out of order, clearly and quickly.

is	vet	of	leg	bad
rub	the	bit	sit	sat
said	this	crash	will	his
I	got	up	my	had

Story 2

I can read the Speed sounds.

I can read the Green words.

I can read the Red words.

I can read the story.

I can answer the questions about the story.

I can read the Speed words.

Story ⭐2 Six fish

Say the Speed sounds

Consonants

*Ask your child to say the sounds (not the letter names)
clearly and quickly, in and out of order. Make sure
he or she does not add 'uh' to the end of the sounds,
e.g. 'f' not 'fuh'.*

f	l ll	m	n	r	s	v	z	sh	th	ng nk

b	c k ck	d	g	h	j	p	qu	t	w	x	y	ch

Each box contains one sound.

Vowels

*Ask your child to say each vowel sound and then the word,
e.g. 'a', 'at'.*

at	hen	in	on	up	day	see	high	blow	zoo

Read the Green words

*For each word ask your child to read the separate sounds, e.g. 'c-a-t',
'f-i-sh' and then blend the sounds together to make the word, e.g. 'cat', 'fish'.
Sometimes one sound is represented by more than one letter, e.g. 'th', 'sh', 'll'.
These are underlined.*

fat cat stop dog fi<u>sh</u> had

pop <u>th</u>at wi<u>ll</u> is

Read the Red words

*Red words don't sound like they look. Read the words out to your child.
Explain that he or she will have to stop and think about how to say the
red words in the story.*

y<u>ou</u> I s<u>ai</u>d of

Story  2
Six fish

Introduction

*This story is about two friends: Pug Dog and Fat Cat. Pug Dog
tells Fat Cat that if he continues to eat so much something
dreadful will happen. And he's right ...*

Fat Cat   Pug Dog

Fat Cat had 1 fish.

Fat Cat had
2 fish.

Fat Cat had 3 fish.

"Stop!" said Pug Dog.

"That is a lot of fish!

You will pop, Fat Cat."

Ask your child:
✨ *Why was Pug Dog worried about Fat Cat?*

"I will not stop,"
said Fat Cat.

"I will not pop."

Fat Cat had 4 fish.

Fat Cat had 5 fish.

Fat Cat had 6 fish.

Pop!

Ask your child:
⭐ *Who was right?*

21

Speed words for Story 2

Ask your child to read the words across the rows, down the columns and in and out of order, clearly and quickly.

fat	you	cat	said	stop
I	dog	of	fish	had
pop	that	will	had	lot
is	fish	fat	pop	not